# The Female
# RUNNER

**Published by WORLD PUBLICATIONS**
**Box 366, Mountain View, CA 94042**

# The Female
# RUNNER

**Recommended Reading:**
*Runner's World Magazine,* $9.50/year
Write for a free catalog of publications
and supplies for runners and other athletes.

© 1974 by
World Publications
P.O. Box 366, Mountain View, CA 94042

Second Printing- December, 1974
Third Printing - March, 1976
Fourth Printing - July 1977

ISBN 089037-037-0

# *Contents*

# *Foreword*

The runner's world is, always has been and will for a long time to come continue to be a man's world. Women only get to sample the leftovers from it.

Women, in the unlikely event that they run at all (they make up more than 50% of the general population but probably less than 1% of the running population), run in shoes designed for men. They race either in meets where men are the star attractions or in meets of their own that no one notices at all. They get what's left of the expense money, prizes and publicity after the men have taken theirs.

Women who run are different from men who run—in ways other than the obvious. The sexes were not created equal, but in the way athletics is set up, we've gone far beyond the inequalities set by chromosomes.

Women are born somewhat weaker and slower than men. But they're compensated with a somewhat better endurance capacity. The difference this makes in the way the sexes run, however, isn't great. The rules of exercise physiology, of training and racing technique, apply almost equally to women and men.

But the rules of society in general and athletic administration in particular split men and women into two camps—the male who is pushed into strenuous sport and the female who is held away. In this society, where sport is a rite of manhood, a young man's virility is suspect if he doesn't compete. A young woman's femininity is questioned if she does compete. The attitude is changing, but only bit by bit. It will be a long time dying.

Social influences, more than physical ones, shape a woman's role in running. The hardest thing for a woman to do, says one of this booklet's contributors, is even to *think* of herself as a runner. Even if she hasn't been brainwashed into thinking the sport isn't healthy for her, she faces other obstacles.

● The fear, often justified, of running alone and being the target of attack—verbal or worse. (More than a few women have been raped while running in public parks.)

● The lack of opportunities for beginners to enter running and receive expert instruction and support. (Men have high school and college teams at every school, and clubs and fitness classes in every major city. Women's programs are considerably harder to find.)

● The lack of opportunities for advanced women to race. (Men's races outnumber women's on the order of 100-1).

Women have to scrape for the things in running which men take for granted—acceptance, encouragement, opportunity. This is the biggest difference between runners of the two sexes. The booklet centers on this and other significant differences, the special problems and newly opening possibilities for women.

*The Female Runner* is designed to help women runners accept the features in their own makeup which separate them from men, and to change the features in the makeup of the sport which keep them from enjoying it equally.

# CHAPTER I

# The Woman As Runner

*"Social pressure—that's the hardest thing we women in track have to overcome. People who see me training are always asking, 'Aren't you a little old to be doing this kind of stuff?' It's very distressing. You would think I was still playing with dolls or something."*

—Francie Larrieu

The hardest step to take is the first one. This is true for all beginning runners, but particularly for women—and most of all mature women. That step for women has obstacles that men don't have in their way.

The main barrier to women runners is the mental one, says Dr. Harmon Brown. Brown coaches female runners in California at the club level, researches the effects of running on them, and has headed a national AAU track and field committee. He thinks the first step, and the hardest to take, is to recognize running as a normal activity for women. Once that hurdle is overcome, the rest—beginning conditioning, progressive increase in training, racing—is relatively simple.

To decide to be a woman runner is to work against the prevailing social current. While it has long since been established that women are physically capable of running anything men can (though perhaps not as fast), the question has another key part to it: Will the women *want* to run or *have the chance* to run the same way?

Unfortunately, the answer in most cases is still no. The rare woman who does run is a strong-minded, independent one who can field challenges and has learned to live with neglect for her side of the sport. For while the reasons for running and the benefits from it are the same for both sexes, the woman is more often called on to defend her reasons and to work harder to claim the benefits.

This isn't to say that all male runners want things this way, or that there is a conspiracy on the part of athletic officials to keep women in their place. This isn't the place for a women's liberation tirade, but only for an explanation of the situation as it is. The first step to correcting inequities is to recognize them as they are— to see which can be changed and how, and which have to be accepted as facts of nature.

It is an uphill struggle all the way for a woman just to show that running is no less normal for her than for a man, that she wants only the same things from it as men, and that she's not simple out there trying to beat the men for the cause of women's lib.

The fact that she runs and races is not in conflict with her womanhood, any more than training and competing prove a man's masculinity.

"I love to run. I love competition," says Francie Larrieu, holder of several world middle-distance records. "Do I look like a muscle-bound monster?" Her dimensions, 5'4" and 100 pounds, and a glance at any photograph of her shows she obviously hasn't been deformed by her years of hard work. Larrieu started running in her early teens and has grown up with the sport.

Bonna Todd didn't have the same opportunity. "I have always loved the outdoors," says the California high school student, "and became interested in running when I was in the fifth grade. When all my friends were playing with jacks, I was in the field jumping hurdles. It was great fun to see just how high I could jump and how fast I could run."

If Bonna had been born a boy, she could have carried on with running through the school's teams. As it was, she quit running because there were no teams for girls. She didn't start again until late high school—when formerly all-male teams were opened to both sexes.

Twenty years earlier, there hadn't even been that small opening into organized running. Patricia Warren writes of the state of the sport when she was in school:

"Oh, how I resent the fact that (an official ) in my high school refused to allow girls' track, instead kept us doing inane calisthenics and girls' basketball. I loved long runs, but I had to do them on the playground, where I could beat almost any boy at a sprint or longer. Had an enlightened coach been around, he might have made a fair cross-country runner out of me.

"College was even worse. There were (instructors) who taught us fencing, modern dance and even how to walk balancing a book on our heads. But no distance running, with all the suberb mental and physical benefits that women can get from it.

"Our society has refused to recognize how badly women need the sanitizing, mind-bending experience of high-stress sports. And it does its best to keep women fretting on minimal levels and wallowing in affluent ease."

In her 30s, Warren "stumbled back into what I wanted to do all along"—which was to run. She says she and other women who run now are "not out for a lark. We're not even merely deadly serious. We are out—each in her own way—to get back something that an over-repressive, over-protective society took away from us."

# 2

# *Coming From Behind*

Women got a late start in sport, and have been running ever since to catch up with the men—not so much in terms of performance but in the distribution of running opportunities.

True, there are still inequities in the way the sexes are treated in athletics, and women almost always end up on the short end of them. It may have taken 25 centuries to make much headway, and women may not be even with men just yet, but they've come a long way and they're still gaining.

Remember that it was a death penalty offense for a woman even to *watch* the ancient Olympics in Greece, let alone to participate. It took the "modern" Olympic organizers 32 years to get around to admitting women to the Games.

Ernst van Aaken, a German physician and running authority, recalls, "After World War I, women were given the right to compete at 50,60 and 100 meters. The 800-meter run was introduced at the 1928 Olympics."

Van Aaken attended the Games at Amsterdam, the first in which women competed at all. He says the 800-meter runners there "were by present standards completely untrained—sprinters trying to find out whether they could finish 800 meters. Prejudice in the male-dominated world of track and field caused the authorities to ban the 800 meters, though neither these men nor medical doctors were equipped to evaluate the events suitability for women."

Not for 32 more years was an event longer than 200 meters included in the Olympics. And not until the 1972 Games in Munich did the women get to go as far as 1500 meters. And with the current emphasis on cutting down the number of events, there isn't much hope that they will race longer than that. The international distance limit holds in spite of mounting evidence that women are better equipped physically for endurance than for sprint events, and are increasingly eager to go farther.

If we accept the premise of this book—that women can run anything men can run but the fastest of them can never go quite as fast as the best men—then it follows that they're entitled to *separate and equal* running programs. This obviously isn't yet the case. The programs in the US as least are either separate and unequal because the women are inherently slower (therefore less worthy of consideration in many minds).

The 1972 US Olympic Trials illustrate "separate and unequal." The men ran in Eugene, Ore. Their meet spread out over 10 days, during which they basked in the adulation of sell-out crowds of 20,000 at nearly every session. It was the best men's meet ever held in the US.

The women, by contrast competed in a two-day Olympic Trials arrange for their own Trials expenses. But in many cases they had an American 1500-meter record there, said later, "I had to sell raffle tickets to get expenses for the Trials. Can you imagine Lyudmila Bragina (Olympic 1500 champion) selling raffle tickets in Russia?"

In fairness to the men, we must note that they, too, has to arrange for their own Trials expenses. But in many cases they had colleges or military organizations footing their bills. Most women are club athletes, and most clubs don't have much money. The men's Trials meet made enough money that it could have paid everyone's expenses. The women's didn't.

Even when meets have both men's and women's events, as hap-

pens in the major US invitationals, the females often are treated
as little more than extra added detractions. Patty Johnson, who
has competed on two Olympic teams and holds most of the American hurdle records, is quite outspoken on this.

Johnson said in an Associated Press interview in early 1974,
"The press and public are only interested in us every four years.
And then they say, 'How come our women don't win more
(Olympic) medals?' "

She's particularly upset over the distribution of prizes and expense money at the invitationals. "The men get things like stereo
sets and radios. And we get these little trophies that cost about
a quarter for a thousand. The meet directors say they're on a
budget and nobody comes to watch the women. That's the same
reason they say they can't afford expense money for more than
a couple of women, while men are being brought in from other
countries."

In 1973, Johnson and Francie Larrieu—the two biggest names
in US women's track at the time—"made a pact that we wouldn't
run if the prizes weren't comparable."

Patty said, "What we needed to make it effective was for no
one to show up. But after I complained to the meet director in
San Francisco, he said next year they'll just have local girls and
not pay anyone's expenses."

For a long time, women have only been getting the crumbs of
the sport. "Did you ever stop to think what a girl who wants to
run has to go through?" wrote Bob Hyten, a women's club coach,
in 1971. "First of all, there are only a half-dozen states that even
tolerate girls' track, in high schools. Next, name a college that
produces women *coaches*, not just health and recreation teachers.
If you are not already frustrated, then notice that only about 60%
of the AAU associations have girls' track."

Hyten pleaded then, "After a decade of verbal concern, it is
now time for everyone to get deeply involved with carrying out
solutions. What the girls need today are meets, clubs, coaches and
research."

In recent years, they have started demanding these and more.
Help has come from an unexpected source—the courts, which
have ruled consistently that runners can't be kept off of teams
simply because they're female.

Tammy Gilpin of Wichita, Kan., is one young woman who went to court when her school wouldn't let her run. Tammy said then, "The boys know I'm not out there just to show off that I can beat them."

Her father said, "We're not women's libbers. We know that boys are stronger than girls, sure. Their records are always better." But he pointed out that if Tammy didn't run with the boys, she'd never compete at all in high school.

The US District Court ruled that the denial of the right to participate "solely on the basis of sex is no longer tolerable under our constitutional concepts."

Schools throughout the country have begun opening their running teams to both sexes. But mixed competition such as this is at best an intermediate step. A *Runner's World* editorial talks of this and further steps:

"A competitive runner must have races. Mixed races are the only opportunity open to hundreds of women. But as a runner advances, he or she needs a test against equals. Mixed competition is inherently unequal, and should only be a step leading to the time when women's programs can stand on their own, apart from men's.

"Mixed racing is a noble beginning but a dead end. For no matter how well a woman runs, she'll never get the attention she deserves if she's back in a pack of men."

*The Sportswoman* magazine, a far more militant publication than *RW*, says basically the same thing:

"Any (law)suit which fights against *distinction* between the sexes will severely hurt the female athlete. She is not a male, and to be forced to compete against males would be like forcing flyweight boxers to fight the heavyweights. It is important to know how fast a woman can run, how far she can throw the javelin or how well a team of women can play. It is not important to discover that a woman can play on a men's 'B' team."

But the magazine's editors qualify this stand by saying that until the women are provided separate programs, that are comparable to men's, women should be allowed to compete on the same teams and in the same events as men.

# 3

# *Separate and Equal*

This is an exciting time to be a woman runner. Though some hurdles still block her path, the prospects facing her have never been better. The push for equal opportunity, though it creates resistance in some quarters, is beginning to show profound effects.

It is becoming clear that opportunity breeds athletes. Women will run if they have the chance and if they see other women running. And in this fact lies the hope for better days ahead. The signs are there from one extreme to the other in both age and distance.

● More than a thousand girls' age-group cross-country runners compete in the national Road Runners Club championships—nearly as many as the boys have, and at the same distance.

● The young women in Iowa show what a high school program can do. Nearly every school in the state has a separate girls' team coach and meets. Thousands of athletes compete in races (at most of the same distances the boys run) leading to a state championship which 10,000 spectators watch.

● Women threaten to shake college athletics to the foundation simply by demanding that females get their fair share of the athletic budget. Here and there, a woman gets a running scholarship. More are bound to qualify as budgets are realigned.

● Marathoning grows from non-existence in the mid-1960s to a legislated-against event at the turn of the decade, to a national championship race for women in 1974. Ten-kilometer and one-hour title runs are on the schedule, too. The long runs appeal to a new class of runner—the woman in her 20s, 30s or older.

The irony of the beautiful situation the young-age-groupers enjoy is this: Boys and girls have the best separate programs at a time in their lives when they need it least. At the RRC cross-country meet in 1972, for instance, girls' winner Robin Campbell ran just two seconds slower than her male counterpart in the 12-13 division. Robin's sister Donna was only a second slower than the boys' champion for 10- and 11-year olds.

The sexes ran separately, which is as it should be in championships for all ages. The point here is, up to age 12 or 13, boys and girls aren't far apart in their abilities to run. As they get older and less alike physically, it's more likely girls will have to run with boys if they want to run at all.

Iowa is an exception there, high school girls are separate. *RW* editor Joe Henderson grew up in Iowa. He says, "They're separate, but not always equal. In the small town where I went to school, and in most other small towns like it, the girls were *superior.* They concentrated on one sport then, basketball, and practiced year-round. At my school the girl's team went to the state tournament twice. And in Iowa, that's a big deal. Fifteen thousand people watched the final game and the winning team makes headlines all over the state on Sunday morning. Where I went to high school, the boys' team was sloppy by comparison. Half the crowd went home after the girls played."

Iowa girls track and cross-country started from scratch in the early 1960s. Now it's so big, a well-funded, professionally staffed Girls' State High School Athletic Association manages the program.

There is nothing comparable to this in the nation's colleges yet. The closest they've come to that is the Association of Intercollegiate Athletics for Women (AIAW), which is very small potatoes beside the rich and powerful National Collegiate Athletic Association.

As recently as 1973, the AIAW national track meet wasn't open to women on track scholarships. It didn't matter much, because there weren't many such women. This is changing. Patty Johnson now is in school on a "full-ride," and so is Francie Larrieu.

No area of women's running, though, has changed faster than the long distances. In 1967, Kathy Switzer created her uproar by running "officially" at Boston—the first woman to do so. At the 1970 AAU convention, the national chairman of women's track dismissed long distances running by females as a "lark." She worried about the physical effects of this kind of running would have on them, and stood by the AAU's opposition to it.

By 1972, Boston has a women's division. By 1973, more than 90 women were breaking four hours in the marathon. By 1974, there was a national championship at this and other long distances.

In retrospect, it appears that the women of the long distances have had the most profound effects of all in changing long-standing attitudes about female runners. They are the oldest, as a rule, and they go the farthest, and because they run in public they're the most visible. Anyone who sees them can see they're thriving on these distances. If they can, anyone can.

Doris Brown Heritage, five-time International cross-country champion, maintains that women are profiting from changing views of running as a whole. She has seen this happen since she started in 1960.

Things are much different from then," she says. "But it has been kind of a slow growth, really. The country's whole attitude about running in general has changed.

"Back when I was in college, I ran around a lake that I've been running around for years. When I first started, I'd come home just about in tears every night because high school guys would push me around and people would say nasty things. It was hard to make myself go out and face all this.

"Now I can hardly run at this place because there are so many joggers and bicyclists and other people that there's just not enough room for a good workout. But it's a pleasant change."

*One of the hardest-dying myths was that women weren't capable of racing long distances like marathons. One of the first to explode it was Sara Mae Berman, running here with her husband Larry at the 1970 Boston Marathon. (Mary Rosenfeld photo)*

# CHAPTER II

# Thinking About Women

### By Dr. Kenneth Foreman

*Dr. Foreman coaches both the men's and women's track teams at Seattle Pacific College, as well as the Falcon Track Club. His best known athlete is Doris Brown Heritage, five-time winner of the International cross-country title. Foreman is a member of the AAU's executive council for women's track and field, and is one of the country's leading authorities on female runners. Foreman's comments first appeared in the US Women's Track Coaches Association newsletter and are reprinted with permission of that organization.*

One of the truly sad things about so potentially a noble activity as sport is the imposition of cultural sanctions and individual prejudices into this dimension of human experience. For example, the classification of sports activities into a masculine-feminine scale reflects discrimination of the worst kind. And yet the fact is that we have employed just this kind of sexual double standard where sport is concerned throughout history. The ancient Greeks beheaded any female who dared watch the warrior athlete perform. In more recent times, females have been psychologically beheaded if they even acted as if they might enjoy vigorous physical activity. While the past 65 years have seen some changes in our attitudes toward the female athlete, most of these changes are a kind of tokenism.

I am reminded of a delightful conversation with two English women a few years ago. They were among the finest female track athletes in Britian. Yet they told of traveling like circus entertainers from city to city where they would enter meets as an added attraction, running for the price of a meal or a night's lodging. Their reminiscing reflected both happiness and sadness— happiness in being able to run, which they dearly loved to do, yet sadness over never really being accepted for who they were or what they could do.

Most girls and women who engage in sport still face this dilemma. A school board member in a large American city recently boasted about his sensitivity to girls athletics by stating that he helped increase their budget 50%, while the boys' budget was only 30% larger than the year before. The girls' budget was $300. The boys': $110,000. Then there was the superintendent of schools who refused to let the girls run cross-country because "they would just go out into the woods and get laid by the boys."

My own experience of working with female athletes is replete with stories of this kind—like being pushed out of a fieldhouse into nine-degree weather when a men's track coach insisted that his afternoon's practice was more important than a national Olympic development clinic for women, or being told by an older professional colleague at a neighboring university that I was a fool to work with female athletes because they were incapable of tolerating stress and would only get into trouble with my male athletes if I let them train together.

The reasons for our attitudes toward women who participate and excel in sport are complicated at best. I submit, however, that for most men the problem is this thing called ego. In western society sport constitutes one of the last frontiers wherein the male can assert his superior strength. For females to engage in sport, or show superiority in the male domain, is an open threat to the male of the species. Perhaps it is understandable that a threatened male would be critical of a female who makes him feel ill at ease with himself. What is not understandable, however, and can no longer be tolerated is the insistence that a female athlete be accepted only on the male's terms—that is, poorly coached, inadequately supported, and publicly recognized only if she passes the "pretty" test.

Prejudice and ignorance have prevented many, if not most, women from participating as freely as they might like in the sport of their choosing. Myths about women have grown out of the prejudices and ignorance.

## MASCULINE-FEMININE MYTHS

A commonly accepted myth is that sports participation has a "masculinizing" influence on female performers. The sad reality about this fallacy is that even those persons who know better find themselves again and again being trapped in situations which support its perpetuation. This often occurs when someone says, "Oh, but she doesn't look like an athlete. She is so pretty." The inference is that she is unique and that unattractive, male-type performers are the rule. The media perpetuates this fallacy. Pictures printed in the newspaper and in sports-oriented publications almost always show only the petite athlete with some comment about how pretty she was when she performed. While coaching the US international team several years ago, I watched the press ignore world class athletes, concentrating their photographic talents on a tall, well-proportioned English girl who was only an alternate in her event.

But the real issue of the masculinizing effect of sport on women goes well beyond superficial comments about who is pretty and who is not. It concerns the deeper significance of what it really means to be either male or female.

The body form of males and females is largely the result of genetic design. Research in this area has shown that heavy training will not alter a female's body form to anywhere near the extent that occurs when males train under like conditions. Other studies have shown a relationship between body builds and types of activities, but there is no evidence that the sport itself influences the build. In other words, a large woman is likely to put the shot; shot putting doesn't create large women. The top women athletes sometimes do have a predominance of "male" physical characteristics and excel for that reason, these characteristics are inherited rather than acquired.

Another side to this issue is the psychological changes which are said to occur when one engages in stressful kinds of physical activity.  The evidence here is neither extensive nor clear-cut.  This stems from the fact that little psychological research has been directed toward women as a group, and that which has been tends to be influenced by cultural expectations for females.  While available evidence does seem to indicate that successsful female athletes are more confident than their less successful sisters, they do assert themselves and they do have courage when engaged in challenging activities, this is not the same as saying that they are becoming males psychologically.  Such evidence does, however, raise serious questions about a society that measures maleness and femaleness by  such arbitrary standards.

## SEXUAL PROBLEMS MYTH

Another myth about the female athlete is that she will somehow become incapable of living out her normal role of sexuality and child-bearing.  Typical of the comments here was made by one school board member when asked his opinion about sports for girls.  He replied, "Oh I think they shoud play so long as they don't get involved competitively and get hard and unfeminine and become incapable of marrying and having children."  There is no evidence whatsoever to support his contention.

Dr. Christine Pickard, consultant on birth control and sex problems refers to female athletes who participated in the Munich Olympics as follows: "Their bodies are important to them.  Women athletes, except for the very rare exceptions, are real women. They are much more interested in sex and physically more responsive than their less active sisters."

Reports from Europe indicate that female athletes marry at an age comparable to the general population, that 75% have their first child before 25 years of age and 90% before their 28th birthday.  A cursory check of the finalists in the last Olympic games reveals that a large number were married, had one or more children and were normal in these respects in their cultural situation.  Data concerned with menstruation, pregnancy and child-birth indicates that female athletes are normal with respect to these functions as well.

On the matter of pregnancy and child-birth, a Hungarian study involving 84 cases among 172 female athletes found complications of pregnancy in lesser precentage than in the control group (non-athletes). Threatened abortions did not exceed the usual average and could not be associated with sport since most stopped their sports activities as soon as their pregnancies were determined. It also was noted that the duration of labor for the female athletes was considerably shorter than among controls.

## INCOMPETENCE MYTH

A third myth about girls and women is that they do not learn as fast or are they capable of performing as well or for as long a duration as men. This fallacy is highlighted by the argument put forth by an athletic director who was defending his policy of forcing girls to practice hockey in a parking lot, using brooms and canes for implements, when he said, "Why pay a coach to teach girls? They can't learn proper technique anyway."

Until recently there was little data concerning the facility with which males and females learned gross motor skills. Comments about the female's learning ability were therefore a matter of conjecture rather than a matter of fact, although evidence is mounting that there is no significant difference between the sexes. Apparent differences again are a manifestation of culture rather than physical potential.

Durability among female athletes is also markedly influenced by culture, i.e., the need of the female to marry and raise a family. However, careful analysis of the top 10 female track and field performers by events in the world in 1972 reveals some interesting information. The range of ages for these 120 world class performers was 16-40 (79 were 25 or older, 26 were 30 or older, and three were over 35). The ranges in ages by event were as follows: sprints 17-33, middle distance 20-32, jumpers 16-34 and throwers 18-40. The figures for world-ranked men aren't significantly different.

## FRAGILE-WOMAN MYTH

Perhaps the most often quoted myth about girls and women is that they are injury prone, mend slowly and seldom will work hard enough to insure complete rehabilitation following an accident. Medical authorities contend that women sustain more soft-tissue injuries than men, especially those concerned with tendons and tendon sheaths—as well as trauma to the bursea and periosteal tissue, and that the primary cause of such injury is ballistic activity such as sprinting and jumping.

I would, however, like to make two observations from my experience. One is my personal belief that women are not more prone to injury than men—and if, anything, they show far more discipline during rehabilitation than men—both in terms of the work that they will do and the pain they will endure. My experience with both sexes dates back more than two decades, and during that time I have seen far more females than males who were willing to pay the price of recovery.

My second comment concerns the incredible disparity between the sexes where medical and para-medical care are concerned. Indeed, if the ratio of trainer and training room supplies to performer is any measure of proneness to injury, one might conclude that boys are almost expected to be injured and girls are not expected to be injured at all. A recent national survey has revealed that fewer than one-tenth of one percent of the colleges and universities in America have any kind of training facility or procedure for female athletes, while more than 99% of these same institutions provide such facilities and programs for males.

There is no question that males and females differ in physical capacities. Females tend to have more fragile skeletal framework. Their ratio of heart weight to body weight is 10-15% less than males. Females have approximately 15% less hemoglobin and 5-7% fewer erythrocytes for a given quantity of blood. The post-pubescent girl possesses only about two-thirds the potential muscle mass as a boy the same age. She has slightly lower oxygen uptake potential and a 2-3 degree higher perspiration threshold.

This combination of factors precludes her from ever competing equally in demanding physical activity with males, to be sure. But the overwhelming weight of evidence indicates that women react to intelligently planned training in the same positive ways that men do. They break down under excessive loads for the same reasons.

The issue here is not whether or not women can compete with men. Females do not want to compete against males. What they do want and are being denied from kindergarten on is the option to compete freely among themselves. There is no valid psycho-biological basis for denying them this chance.

OM Photo

# CHAPTER III

# Basic Differences

*"We women long distance runners notice that nobody worries publicly about the effects of long-distance efforts on men, nor is anyone using it as a pretext to curb men's activities. Yet, imagine that temporary effect that a marathon in 90-degree heat must have on a couple of hundred guys' ability to be a father."*

**—Patricia Warren**

The most obvious differences between the sexes are the ones relating directly to sexual roles. The fear that sports would scramble the delicate insides of women and keep them from becoming mothers was the excuse used for a long time to keep them out of things like running. It's clear now, however, that her womanhood need only limit her physically when she's in late pregnancy and immediately afterward. (See more on this in the last section of this chapter.)

Having babies is only a temporary curb on a woman's ability to run. No other curbs are any more justified for them than for men. Even though the two sexes are put together somewhat differently, they react in approximately the same way to running.

"From the physiological point of view," says Dr. Harmon

Brown, "females can participate in the same sports as males."
The question no longer is *whether* they can compete, but how
their sex differences influence the *way* they compete.

"It is important for the athlete, coach and official to be aware,"
writes distance runner Janet Heinonen, "of physiological differences which indicate that men and women cannot compete together *on an equal basis.*" She summarizes the findings of exercise physiologist Herbert A. de Vries:

● "The differences in sports performance can be attributed
partially to the ratio of strength to weight—which (after puberty)
is normally greater in the male. Women have a smaller pro-
portion of muscles in relation to a considerably larger amount
of adipose (fatty tissue).

● "The ratio of heart weight to body weight in women ages
10-60 is also a factor limiting sports performance. Women have
only 85-90% the heart size of men.

● "Males have a higher basal metabolic rate. But when evalu-
ated in relationship to muscle mass instead of surface area, sex
differences disappear.

● "Men have an advantage in blood content. Many women
are chronically anemic due to an iron deficiency. Men in the
age group 20-30 have, on the average, 15% more hemoglobin per
100 milliliters of blood and 6% more erythrocytes per cubic
millimeters. This combination of factors gives men a greater
capacity to carry oxygen.

● "Women have a lower 'erbo-lungs quotient,' which indicates
the degree an individual must encroach on her anaerobic re-
serves to perform at a given level.

● "Cardiac cost, the measure of stress on the heart for a
given workload, shows that girls 12-13 work most efficiently.
There is not further improvement with increasing age. The male,
on the other hand, at age 12-13, has only one-third the cardiac
capacity of males in the 31-36 age group.

● "Maximum oxygen consumption peaks at an early age in
women too. Eight- and nine-year olds have the highest oxygen
consumption, then they decline to age 15; after that it remains
constant. Boys peak at 15-16 and maintain that level through
young adulthood.

● "By far the greatest percentage of injuries (among women)
is found in sports that require explosive efforts, short runs (52%)

and the long jump (31%). It is difficult to avoid the conclusion, says de Vries, that such activities are not suited to the females' musculo-skeletal system."

By no means, however, are these conclusions accepted as gospel in athletic medical circles. The writer Heinonen herself says, "In future studies, serious questions must be posed to determine the difference between biological constraints and societal/environmental constraints. Do females have more fatty tissue because of the role they play in society—that of the 'weaker' sex? Are females as slow by nature as the world track records indicate or is it due to the fact that proportionately fewer women compete in athletics?"

Researcher Jack Wilmore of the University of California in Davis says the physical difference between the sexes are "more apparant than real." He says there are indeed the differences de Vries mentions when untrained males and females are the test subjects. But when they are trained athletes, women test out much closer to men.

German Dr. Ernst van Aaken writes, "It has been asserted and supported with nice statistics that women have smaller hearts (then men). But what was forgotten was that women have for hundreds of years lived in the seclusion of household work." When they get out of the house and train, he says, their hearts catch up.

Van Aaken has maintained for more than 25 years that women are ideally suited biologically for races like the marathon. He was saying this and being dismissed as a crank, at a time when they didn't compete beyond 200 meters in the Olympics.

"The athletically most important difference between men and women," according to van Aaken, "is that 40% of a man's body mass is muscle compared to only 23% for women. The only muscle which both men and women can train in equal measure is the heart. It is even possible that women have a relative advantage here (in their muscle endurance characteristics) because the muscles of women work slowly and men's muscles are generally more suited to explosive functions."

Van Aaken's time finally came in 1973, when he was allowed to host the first German women's marathon championship—the first race of its kind in the world.

# 6

# *Training Application*

### *By Dr. Joan Ullyot*

*Dr. Ullyot, a physician specializing in physiology and pathology, began running when she was 30. Two years later she was running marathons (she has done 3:13). Her writing here centers on applying physiological knowledge to the practical running situation—particularly with older beginning runners of the type she teaches in San Francisco.*

The topic of physiology can be summarized briefly: Women are different from men in their physical endowment. In general, they have less muscle mass, lighter bone structure and more fat. Thus, they will usually weigh less than a man of the same height, and will also have less power to propel the same mass.

In view of this hormonally-determined sex difference, it is ironic that women athletes were limited to sprint events for so many years. The sprints require power and speed—muscle-dependent attributes—more than stamina and efficiency of movement. It is in the latter characteristics that the average light-

33

framed, slim female runner excels (as does the small, lean male distance runner).

In short, women are made to run long rather than fast. While I doubt that women will ever come closer than 20 seconds to the men's mile record, there is no such limitation in their ability to go long distances—frequently longer than men, as 100-milers Natalie Cullimore and Miki Gorman, and 50-miler Eileen Waters.

Another physical factor that may influence running is the slightly wider pelvis and hip span in many women. The best women runners usually have narrow hips—like the men. This probably influences both efficiency and speed, because the individual with wider hips must shift the center of gravity more with each step to bring the weight over the head of the femur, where it belongs. Thus, some energy which could be used for forward propulsion must be diverted to a side-to-side motion, resulting in slightly decreased efficiency of stride. However, this difference is usually small, and other peculiarities of stride probably detract just as much from efficiency (in both men and women).

Women generally have fewer total red blood cells than men. This is probably another of those hormonally-determined differences we can't do anything about. It also means that women can't carry as much oxygen as men, and on this basis alone will generally have a lower aerobic capacity. Jack Wilmore has found that top women runners have high maximal oxygen uptake values, but these values would probably be still higher if more hemoglobin were available.

Add to this lower hemoglobin the fact that many women are chronically iron deficient because they don't replace the monthly blood loss, and you get a limit on oxygen carrying capacity which can seriously reduce running performance. I think all women should take a daily iron supplement to make sure their bodies will manufacture as many red cells as possible. Still, it would take the equivalent of a "blood-doping" transfusion of at least a pint to put the average woman on a par with the average man.

When women start to run, both physique and society-influenced life style cause them more difficulties than male beginners. Not only are bones and muscles weaker in women than in men, but years of relative inactivity have resulted in under-exercised, semi-atrophied tendons and ligaments. The result: sprained ankles, tendinitis, shin splints and other "overuse" injuries tend to occur early in the running program when they can discourage the beginner.

These troubles are *not* due to inborn sex differences so much as to the fact that most women never run around after age 10-12. (I doubt that we will see these problems in the new generation of age-groupers, whose ligaments are as strong as anyone's.) We see similar injuries in older men who start running after years of inactivity. It's just that women reach this point of atrophy at age 20, men at age 40.

Long years of wearing high heels have shortened the achilles tendons markedly in some older women. Anyone who has been teetering around on spikes regularly should be extra careful. Similarly, years of wearing skirts—and thus having restricted knee movement—lead, in my opinion, to another peculiarity seen most frequently in older women: a gait in which the leg is brought from back to front by swinging the foot out to the side instead of lifting the knee. This is not at all efficient or speedy.

A good beginning running program can prevent injuries by insisting on proper footwear, heel-first or flat-footed running style, strengthening exercises for the ankles, stretching for the achilles and gradual progression in running. No matter how well conditioned a woman's heart and lungs may be, it is not wise for her to run more than a mile at a time for 2-3 weeks. The time is necessary to adjust to the new stresses.

The most common single injury, in my experience, seems to be a stress-induced tendinitis on the outside of the foot and ankle. The injury looks and feels like a sprained ankle. However, there is no history of a sudden wrench: the swelling just appears. I had it myself in my first few months.

The beginning woman runner always asks, "Will I lose weight?" Answer: probably not, but you will redistribute it and firm up. Any woman who loses weight with our program has dieted to do so. The men, suprisingly, often lose weight along with inches, without dieting. The sex difference may result from different eating patterns. In rats, males that are exercised don't increase their caloric intake to match the energy spent. Females, however, eat more and don't lose. They compensate perfectly for the calories worked off. If this is true of humans as well as rats, it would account for the observed pattern of weight losses among runners.

Regarding mere advanced training, I think women can run just as hard and long as men, but perhaps should avoid the short, fast intervals which can lead to injury (lighter frame, remember?). Personally, I favor Lydiard-type training based on endurance runs followed by sharpening with frequent races to peak.

My training motto is "go long rather than fast," and we use this principle in my classes. Whenever anyone feels ready to advance, we encourage them to run farther and not worry about increasing speed. (Faster time, of course, comes with better conditioning anyway.) This helps prevent injuries and promote enjoyment of running. If you like it, you want to do more of it, not get it over with faster, right?

In our groups, the women grasp this idea right from the start, but we have occasional troubles persuading the men to stop working on a six-minute mile and join us on our eight-minute outings The men tend to be much more speed conscious, trying to show themselves what good shape they're in, I guess.

# 7

# *About Motherhood*

Paola Cacchi and Joyce Smith finished one-two in the 1973 International cross-country championships. Both had their careers interrupted earlier by child-bearing.

Judy Ikenberry and Marilyn Paul were the first two finishers in the AAU women's marathon in 1974. Ikenberry is the mother of three children and Paul has a young son.

The victories for motherhood would make a long list. But these few examples are enough to show that women who decide to have babies don't have to forget about high-level athletics. The Cacchis and Ikenberrys are putting to rest fears over, "What effect will running have on my ability to have a healthy baby?" and the opposite of that, "What effect will having a baby have on my ability to run?"

The physical effects, it appears, are not much different than those a man might have if he underwent surgery and needed a long layoff to recover. He would have a setback, of course, but could be confident of coming back to run at least as far as ever.

Roberta Angeloni, a top Canadian middle-distance runner and

a columnist for *Sports and Fitness Instructor,* writes, "Without doubt pregnancy does have some effects on the quality and quantity of sports performance, just as sports performance also affects the pregnancy. But most of the (scientific) literature suggests that the effects are positive and to the benefit of the mother-athlete."

She reviews the work of Hungarian Dr. Gyula Erdelyi, who has studied 172 female athletes with children:

● "Two-thirds of the athletes continued their usual sports activities during the first three to four months of their pregnancies. The quality of their performances did not decrease during the first trimester (three months). Most of them stopped their activity during or after the fourth month of pregnancy mainly because of decreased efficiency and performance.

● "Complications of labor and delivery did not exceed the usual average. On the contrary, the necessity of Caesarian section was 50% less in the athletic group than in the control group of non-athletes. The duration of labor was shorter than average for 87% (of the athletes)."

Angeloni also reports that German scientists who surveyed a number of running mothers "found an increase in strength, endurance and tenaciousness" in those who returned to their sports after delivering children.

Janet Heinonen writes that several women have won Olympic medals while in early pregnancy, and that "one prominent distance runner whom I know nearly delivered her healthy son at the track."

A distance runner from Colorado, Marcia Le Mire, tells of her experience while pregnant and while nursing:

"I would like more female runners to know that neither of these conditions precludes running. I ran for nine months of my first pregnancy, with complete approval from my doctor, and seven months with my second pregnancy. Distances ranged from three to seven miles. I also began running again shortly after delivery (one and two weeks).

"Many women feel exercise cuts down milk supply and therefore do not run and nurse at the same time. They do one or the other. This need not happen. I ran a marathon (3:53) when my first child was 10 months old and still nursing."

Apparently the bigger problem for a mother of a young child

38

is simply finding the time to get out of the house to run.

The problem facing a woman who is menstruating is simply getting the enthusiasm to do it when she feels blah. There is little evidence from women as a group that the menstrual period seriously affects performance. Women in all stages of their monthly cycle won medals at the Tokyo Olympics, according to Bulgarian researcher E. Zacharieva.

Zacharieva surveyed 66 women. One out of three said she always trained during menses, and 53% reported training "sometimes." However, two-thirds of the women said they competed regardless. Of the Olympic athletes, 37% said their performance didn't change; 28% said the effects varied; 16% said the effect was "always bad," 15% "bad the week before," 3% "always good."

These women were divided almost evenly between those reporting no change in their feeling of fitness and those who said they felt weak and nervous and not too interested in running on those days.

# CHAPTER IV

# Hard Headed Runners

*"I do believe that women may take less kindly to coaching than men. At least we older types are that way. Is this a peculiar feminine trait? I doubt it. It's still such an individual decision for a woman to start running—rather than the expected activity— that this selects mainly the more independent and less teachable types. In short, maybe we have to be stubborn and thick-skinned to start. So it's no surprise if we stay that way."*

—**Joan Ullyot**

In the social environment as it is now, a woman athlete has to be independent and hard-headed just to buck the prevailing mythology. Some of the traits that allow her to do this are acquired, some are inherited. We won't attempt to guess which, but simply to draw a phychological profile of the woman who runs.

Before getting to a professional psychologist's appraisal and to a woman runner's view, listen to what three males who coach females have to say:

● **Ernest van Aaken**—"Psychologically, men are more explosive, inconstant, not enduring, and in pain and exertion—especially among high-performance athletes—somewhat snivelling. Women are the opposite: tough, constant, enduring, level and calm under the pain to which her biology exposes her (during child-birth). On the average, she is more patient than men. Armed with these advantages, women are in a position to do endurance feats previously considered impossible."

● **Bob Hyten**—"The major difference in the sexes lies in their psychological makeup. While it was long ago determined that women *could* endure more pain than men, this does not mean they *will*. While society urges a boy to endure hardship for athletic success, it does not ask that of a girl. In fact, it probably discourages mental strength by thinking of all girls as soft and emotionally weak."

● **Pat Lanin**—"The girls seem to have fewer sex-identity problems than boy do. An adolescent boy often has a complex array of motives directing him toward running—not the least of which is the desire to prove his masculinity through sport. Girls have the compulsion to prove themselves through sport in a similiar fashion, but the identity problem here is of the opposite nature. The girl's self-concept of her female sexuality may be challenged by peers or family if she participates in such a demanding activity."

The women who have come into sports so far are generally physically talented to begin with. Their justification for competing is that they're good at it. In the same way, sports also select women who are able to stand on their own psychologically and don't much care what others think of them. They're opening the way to full acceptance for their less talented, more sensitive sisters.

# *The New Dimension*

### *By Hugh Bowen*

*Dr. Thomas Tutko, whom Hugh Bowen interviewed for this article, co-directs (with Dr. Bruce Ogilvie) the Institute for the Study of Athletic Motivation at San Jose State University. When he was interviewed, Tutko was writing a book on the psychological aspects of women in sports.*

The psychological obstacles still in the path of women athletes are considerable. Dr. Thomas Tutko says, "To go into athletics a woman must be rejected by men. She must be rejected by women."

The women on any block, if they are "passive, quiet, unassuming and subservient" may critize the female athlete severly, Tutko says, because they themselves are "threatened." Some men, of course, are also threatened. Sport is a "male world," according to the psychologist, where young men test themselves in a "ritual of manhood," and mature men affirm their manhood. As

43

Tutko points out, "Men get embarrassed when women do better, or do well." But the men's reaction may also be more harsh. "The most subtle way and the most penetrating, I think, of eliminating women, is to indicate that to participate in this male world a woman must be queer, lesbian."

As if all this weren't enough, "the majority of families find it very hard to accept that their daughter is an athlete" Tutko has found.

Yet women compete, women run, in ever increasing numbers. The women who lead the way are strong-minded. Tutko's tests of superior male and female athletes "show them to be on the high end of the (personality) scale. In some cases, they are extraordinarily well put together—the women particularly."

Top women athletes are even more "autonomous" and independent" than their male counterparts. They show greater self-reliance, "less need for sensitive understanding and involvement with others." Dr. Bruce Ogilvie, Tutko's associate, explains, "We attribute this to the cultural repression of women. To succeed in any field, a woman has to be able to stand up and spit in the eye of those in charge."

Fortunately, the stereotypes which hold back women in athletics are cracking. Billie Jean King is a model for breaking myths, according to Tutko. "She's not homely, she's pretty. Not only is she talented, she's extra talented. She's a top competitor, and she's married. She doesn't hang around totally with women, she's successful from a money standpoint, she looks feminine, she acts feminine."

The prevailing attitude has been that sports participation is contrary to femininity. But it may be that the two will act in harmony, women's sports adding a new dimension to femininity. Tutko predicts that this new dimension will consist of "women being physically trim, being physically fit, the ability to integrate successful athletics with your life. No longer is she expected to be passive. You can respect her opinion. She's been there. She can be vocal. She can be independent any time she wants to. She can try to win in sport. She can be tough. To be successful in female sports, you now don't have to be like a man."

Women may well change the world of sports for the better. First, they seem to go into it for different and perhaps more positive reasons than do men. Tutko's evidence, though it is uncertain and speculative at this point, suggests that for female athletes "there seemed to be a much closer identification with, and love for, father. Women may go into sports because they feel closely attached to a strong male figure, who is also the father. But males go into sports and stay in sports primarily because of fear of rejection and punishment by the parents."

Dr. Tutko thinks the typical male response to success is constrained. "You're never supposed to say, 'Yeah, I really did well, and I'm really proud of what I did.' You're supposed to act humble and resolve to do better. Never be satisfied. That's neurotic behavior. That's drinking salt water, and it's never going to quench your thirst. Women, on the other hand, seem to show a greater degree of joy and freedom, spontaneously. They are happy spontaneously a lot more. I think because they are trained along these lines."

He continues, "Women can add a graceful dimension to sport, where you can be concerned with how they perform rather than just the final score. Males seem to be so oblivious, so out of tune and so numb. There will be a merging of the two (male and female attitudes toward sports). The reason that male sports cannot be creative is that they are totally preoccupied and obsessed with discipline. Limits. Orderliness. Efficiency. Rules."

While Dr. Tutko and I were mulling over the labyrinthine psychological problems facing female athletes, a woman popped into his office.

"Hey," she said, "it's not unfeminine to do sports; I ran track in high school, and I'm proud of the muscles I developed."

Insisting that we were only discussing the problems, not supporting them, I asked if she didn't feel the need to understand the difficulties, to reconcile her femininity and her sports?

"No, I just do it because it makes me feel wonderful, and makes me feel competent."

Better times are coming.

# 10

---

# Possible Conflicts

### By Patricia Warren

*Long distance runner Pat Warren is an editor with Readers'
Digest and the author of several books.*

It would be a cliche to list yet again the benefits of running
for women. They are the same as for men, with the added possi-
bility of better gynecological health.

But in our excitement at opening up this great sport for the
women of the 1970s, we sometimes overlook two dangers. And
they are real dangers, compared to the mythical tipped uteruses
that the AAU used to imagine for us.

Running *could* be a bad thing for an individual woman—de-
spite the physical good it does her. Sport is like anything else in
life that demands proper handling: career, drugs, religion, children. If it's managed right, it can glow in her life like a stone in its
proper setting. If it runs wild, it can create a lot of problems. It
can even—like anything else—destroy.

The first danger is the new independence of mind that running forges in us. Judging by my wide acquaintance with women runners, running awakens in a woman whole areas of mind that were dormant before. Because it's such a demanding sport, it awakens them in a very emphatic way. Once awakened, these qualities of mind really drive us. Even when it is carefully managed, this new independence, this new toughness is going to change us. With all this raw new strength and power available to us, there is no way that our heads and our lives are going to be the same.

I am thinking of a number of women runners who, in the past few years, have found their personal relationships greatly changed by running—most crucially, their relationships with boy friends and husbands. Sometimes the change made for warmer, more meaningful male-female relationships, especially if the male was a runner, too. Sometimes it didn't, and the woman in question found herself single again. One would have to know each case intimately to know whether running mercifully hastened the end of a bad relationship or whether it destroyed a good one. But the fact is certain: running put these women's feet, literally, on a new road that led them to a changed life.

The second danger is that running can put extra pressure on a woman at a time in her life when she doesn't need extra pressure. God knows, these are heavy times for everybody. But women, particularly, are reacting to strange new pressures. They find themselves being told that they must re-enrich and re-evaluate their lives. Or they spontaneously feel the urge to do this.

To every woman, lately, there comes that moment when she feels she's going to lose her marbles. If on top of this she adds a hearty 60-70 miles a week or a heavy schedule of races, running might be the thing that breaks her down. In the right circumstances, it only exhausts you more.

If a woman finds this is the case then it's probably a moment to back off, take an honest look at the stress load she's carrying, and do some drastic cutting here and there. Maybe 30 miles a week is a saner way to life for a while. Or maybe she should lighten her race schedule, or even drop it for one season.

Over the few years I've spent on the running scene, I've noticed that a lot of people—both men and women—have gone through the same cycle. They start with an almost religious fervor for running. They get into it more and more heavily, peak for a while. Then, suddenly, when it comes to overall commitments, they find themselves in over their noses. They find that they have to draw back a little and re-order their priorities.

The reasons I saw were various. One woman had to escape destructive pressures in athletic competition for a while. A man I know had to bow out of heavy running and heavy athletic politics for a little, and give his head a tonic by doing some neglected research for his career. But all the reasons seemed to have one thing in common: running was taking over too much.

The woman who enters running now has many attractive choices open to her. Now that the AAU has liberalized its rules, she can run almost as freely as the men. She can find her own level in the sport. She can be an age-group cross-country superstar, or an over-40s regular in the local marathons, or a pioneer 100-miler, or just a run-on-the-beach type like me. The only limits will be her ambition and natural talents.

But she will need to find the level in her own life that running will work best at. The new heightening awareness of women everywhere will help her to do this successfully. Then, and only then, will running be in practice what we always preached it was in ideal: a good thing for both body and mind.

## RECOMMENDED READING

Below is a list of several books that can be most helpful to all women runners.

*Women's Running* by Joan Ullyot
*The Complete Runner* by *RW* Editors
*Jog, Run, Race* by Joe Henderson
*Dr. Sheehan on Running* by George Sheehan
*Running Foot Doctor* by Steve Subotnick

For a complete catalog of running books write to *Runner's World*, Box 366, Mountain View, CA 94042. Also recommended is *Runner's World* Magazine at the same address. Sample copies on request.